Colin is fed up. He has no money until his Jobseeker's Allowance goes into his bank account on Friday.

Jack has been sorting out his room. There are lots of things he doesn't need any more.

"Don't leave all that rubbish there. I've just tidied up," says Mum.

"What shall I do with it all?" Jack asks.

Jack explains that he has been tidying his room. This is all the stuff he doesn't want any more. He doesn't know what to do with it.

Colin has a brilliant idea to make some money.

I know! Let's do a car boot sale and sell some of our stuff.

Kim and Colin decide to clear out their rooms so they have things to sell too.

On Sunday everyone gets up early to drive to the car boot sale. Dad has been to the bank and got some change for a float.

They set up their table. Soon people start to look at the things they have for sale. Mum and Dad go off to see if there is anything they want to buy from the other stalls.

Colin keeps his money in his pocket. "It will be safe there," he thinks.

Jack has his money in a tin.

Kim has hers in a bum bag.

Soon they are selling their things. One man asks if they will put a CD aside for him. He has no cash and needs to go and get some. He's going to the bank to use the hole in the wall.

A police officer comes by to warn them that there are pickpockets around.

As soon as the police officer has gone, Jack notices something odd.

Somebody is taking money from the pocket of one of the customers.

The pickpocket runs away, but the police officer chases after him.

The police officer arrests the pickpocket. Everybody is pleased that Jack noticed what was going on.

On the way home Colin, Kim and Jack count their money.

"That was a good morning's work," says Mum, "In more ways than one!"

Don't forget to give me the float money back!